Foundations for Algebra: Year 2
Tool Kit

Managing Editors:

Elizabeth Coyner
   Bear River School
Beverly Brockhoff
   Glen Edwards Middle School

Illustrator:

Jonathan Weast
   Weast & Weast Illustration Studio
   Sacramento, California

Technical Assistance:

Bethany Sorbello
   CPM Educational Program
Thu Pham
   The CRESS Center
   University of California, Davis

Developed by CPM Educational Program

Program Directors:

Judith Kysh
   Departments of Mathematics and Education
   San Francisco State University
Tom Sallee
   Department of Mathematics
   University of California, Davis
Brian Hoey
   CPM Educational Program

v 3.0

Foundations for Algebra: Year 2

Introduction to the Tool Kit

This booklet contains all of the statements of mathematical definitions, properties, and ideas from the course. It is called a "Tool Kit" because the information in it is what you will use to solve the problems in the textbook and to master the ideas of the course. The Tool Kit is an important part of your course notes. The authors expect you to complete the questions after every Tool Kit problem in the textbook to help you understand each idea. By doing so you will also improve your study skills.

These booklets are consumable, so you are encouraged to make additional notes in them and to put examples in the Tool Kit that will help you understand and use the ideas in the course. Your teacher will give you additional information about ways to use your Tool Kit and when it is to be used during class. The authors recommend that you have it available whenever you are working on math problems. Once you master the use of the "tools," you will almost certainly be successful in this course.

Credits for the First Edition

Heidi Ackley
Steve Ackley
Elizabeth Baker
Bev Brockhoff
Ellen Cafferata
Elizabeth Coyner
Scott Coyner
Sara Effenbeck
William Funkhouser

Brian Hoey
Judy Kysh
Kris Petersen
Robert Petersen
Edwin Reed
Stacy Rocklein
Kristie Sallee
Tom Sallee
Howard Webb

Technical Assistance

Jennifer Buddenhagen
Grace Chen
Janelle Petersen

David Trombly
Erika Wallender
Emily Wheelis

5 6 7 8 9 10 11 12   09 08 07 06 05

Printed in the United States of America   ISBN 1-931287-20-1

Where to Find Things

>>Continued on the next page.>>

Where to Find Things (continued)

GO-8

STUDY TEAM GUIDELINES

1. Each member of the team is responsible for his or her own behavior.

_____

_____

_____

GO-20

STUDY TEAM GUIDELINES

2. Each member of the team must be willing to help any other team member who asks for help.

GO-29

STUDY TEAM GUIDELINES

3. When you have a question ask your partner or team first. If no one can answer the question, then ask the teacher for help.

_____

_____

_____

_____

_____

_____

GO-44

STUDY TEAM GUIDELINES

4. Use your team voice.

_____

_____

_____

A COMPLETE GRAPH

Graphs are ways of displaying and comparing information.
A complete graph has the following characteristics:

• All graphs are **neat** and easy to read and, when appropriate, constructed with a **straightedge**.

• The units (or numbers) along the axes are clearly **labeled**.

• The axes (the vertical and horizontal number lines) are labeled with **words** that explain the numbers on the axes.

• The units (numbers marked on the axes) follow **equal intervals** on each axis.

• All graphs have a **title**.

• A key or **legend** is included when it is necessary to explain any symbols that are used in the graph.

Graphs should be drawn on graph paper or resource pages.

COMMON MEASUREMENTS

Length
12 inches = 1 foot
36 inches = 1 yard
3 feet = 1 yard
5, 280 feet = 1 mile

Volume (fluid)
8 ounces = 1 cup
16 ounces = 1 pint
2 pints = 1 quart
4 quarts = 1 gallon

Weight
16 ounces = 1 pound
2,000 pounds = 1 ton

Temperature
Fahrenheit		Celsius
212°	Water Boils	100°
98.6°	Body Temperature	37°
72°	Room Temperature	22°
32°	Water Freezes	0°

Time
60 seconds = 1 minute
60 minutes = 1 hour
24 hours = 1 day
7 days = 1 week
365 days = 1 year
52 weeks = 1 year

Centuries
1800's = 19th century
1900's = 20th century
2000's = 21st century

INTERVALS, SCALING AND THE NUMBER LINE

The numbers on the axes of a graph show the **SCALING** of the axes.
The difference between consecutive markings tells the size of the
INTERVAL. When you scale each axis you must use <u>equal</u> intervals
to represent the data accurately. For example, an interval of 5 creates a
scale numbered 0, 5, 10, 15, etc. Unequal intervals distort the
relationship in the data.

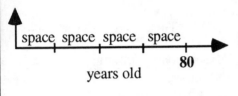

years old

Notice on the graph at left that
80 marks the end of the *fourth*
interval. If you divide 80 years
by 4 you can see the length of
an interval on this graph is 20
$(80 \div 4 = 20)$.

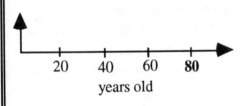

years old

The second graph at left has
each interval marked. We call
this "scaling the axis."

The most fundamental graph
is the **NUMBER LINE**.
It represents all the numbers
you will use in this course.

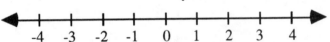

While integer intervals are shown, fractions, π, square roots, and other
numbers can be placed in the corresponding intervals.

MEAN, OUTLIERS, and RANGE

The **MEAN** is the arithmetic average of a data set. One way to determine the mean is to add all values in a set of data and divide the sum by the number of values.

Example: Find the mean of this set of data: 38, 42, 50, 40, and 35.
- $38 + 42 + 50 + 40 + 35 = 205$
- $205 \div 5$ (the number of values) $= 41$, so the mean is 41.

OUTLIERS are numbers in a data set that are either much higher or much lower than the other numbers in the set.

Example: Find the outlier of this set of data: 88, 90, 96, 93, 87, 12, 85, and 94.
The outlier is 12.

The **RANGE** of a set of data is the difference between the maximum (highest value) and minimum (lowest value).

Example: Find the range of this set of data: 114, 109, 131, 96, 140, and 128.
- The highest value is 140.
- The lowest value is 96.
- $140 - 96 = 44$, so the range is 44.

The mean is generally the best measure of central tendency to use when the set of data does not contain outliers.

SOLVING PROBLEMS WITH
GUESS AND CHECK TABLES

- Read the problem carefully. Make notes or sketch a picture to organize the information in the problem.

- Look at the question being asked. Decide what you are going to guess. Set up a table. Leave extra space for more columns in case you need them.

- Calculate the entry for a column and label the column.

- Continue the table until the check is correct.

- Write the answer in a complete sentence.

Example: The sum of two consecutive numbers is 29. What are the numbers?

Guess First Number	Second Number	Total of Numbers (Sum)	Check 29
10	(10) + 1 = 11	(10) + (11) = 21	too low
20	(20) + 1 = 21	(20) + (21) = 41	too high
15	(15) + 1 = 16	(15) + (16) = 31	too high
14	(14) + 1 = 15	(14) + (15) = 29	correct

The sum of the two consecutive numbers 14 and 15 is 29.

STEM-AND-LEAF PLOT

A **STEM-AND-LEAF PLOT** is a way to display data that shows the individual values from a set of data and how the values are distributed. The "stem" part of the graph represents the leading digit of the number. The "leaf" part of the graph represents the other digit(s) of the number.

Example: Students in a math class received the following scores on their test:
49, 52, 54, 58, 61, 61, 67, 68, 72, 73, 73, 73, 78, 82, and 83. Display the test score data on a stem-and-leaf plot.

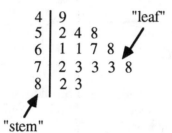
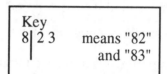

```
4 | 9              "leaf"
5 | 2 4 8
6 | 1 1 7 8
7 | 2 3 3 3 8
8 | 2 3
```
"stem"

Key
8 | 2 3   means "82"
            and "83"

MEASURES OF CENTRAL TENDENCY

Numbers that locate or approximate the "center" of a set of data are called **MEASURES OF CENTRAL TENDENCY.** The mean, median, and mode are three measures of central tendency.

The **MEAN** is the arithmetic average of the data set. (See problem GO-30.) The mean is generally the best measure of central tendency to use when the set of data does not contain outliers.

The **MEDIAN** is the middle number in a set of data <u>arranged</u> <u>numerically</u>. If there is an even number of values, the median is the mean of the two middle numbers. The median is more accurate than the mean as a measure of central tendency when there are outliers in the data set.

The **MODE** is the value in a data set that occurs more often than any other value. Data sets may have more than one mode, and some do not have any mode. (See problem GO-43(d).) The mode is useful when the data are not numeric, such as showing a "most popular" choice.

Suppose the following data set represents the number of home runs hit by the best seven players on a major league baseball team: 16, 46, 21, 9, 13, 15, and 9.

The mean is $\dfrac{16 + 46 + 21 + 9 + 13 + 15 + 9}{7} = \dfrac{129}{7} \approx 18.43$.

The median is 15, since, when arranged in order—9, 9, 13, 15, 16, 21, 46—the middle number is 15.

The mode is 9, since it occurs twice and no other number appears more than once.

QUARTILES AND BOX-AND-WHISKER PLOTS

To find **QUARTILES**, the data set must be in order from smallest to largest. First find the median of the entire data set. Next find the median of the lower half of the data set. Finally, find the median of the upper half of the data set. The quartiles are the medians of the upper and lower halves of the data set.

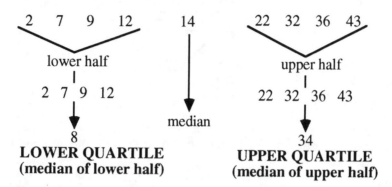

A **BOX-AND-WHISKER PLOT** displays data using quartiles. The plot and its parts appear below using the data above as a model. Problem GO-56 has the step-by-step directions for how to create a box and whisker plot.

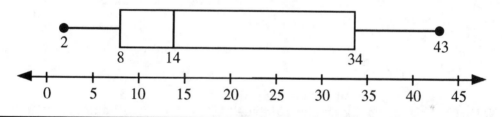

Make your notes about quartiles and box-and-whisker plots in the space below.

GRAPHING POINTS ON AN XY-COORDINATE GRID

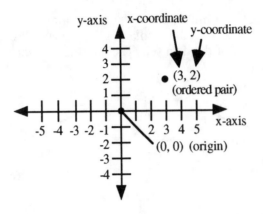

Numerical data that you want to put on a two-dimensional graph is entered on the graph as **POINTS**.

The points on the graph are identified by two numbers, which together make an **ORDERED PAIR** written generally as (x, y). For example, (3, 2). These two numbers are called **COORDINATES** because together they name the location of the point on the graph.

The first number of the ordered pair is the **X-COORDINATE** because it represents the horizontal distance from (0, 0).

The second number of the ordered pair is the **Y-COORDINATE** because it represents the vertical distance from (0, 0).

The ordered pair (3, 2) is located at a point that is right 3 units and up 2 units from the **ORIGIN**, (0, 0). The scaled lines are called the **X-AXIS** (horizontal) and **Y-AXIS** (vertical).

Make your notes for parts (a) and (b) in the space below.

GRAPHING TERMS

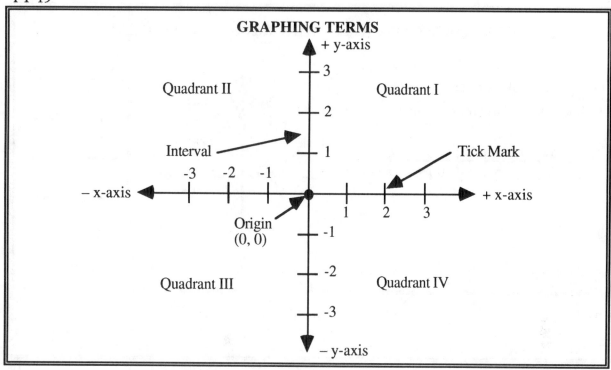

Answer parts (a) through (c) in the space below.

_____

_____

_____

_____

FT-44

ABSOLUTE VALUE

ABSOLUTE VALUE is the distance a number is from zero on the number line in either direction. We use the symbol $|x|$ to indicate the absolute value of any number x. For example,

$$|-3| = 3 \text{ and } |3| = 3.$$

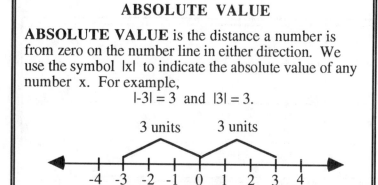

_____

_____

_____

_____

_____

COMPONENTS OF A LINEAR GRAPH

- and y-axes labeled and scaled
- equation (rule) written near the line
- line extended as far as possible

x	-1	0	1	2	3	x
y	2	4	6	8	10	y = 2x + 4

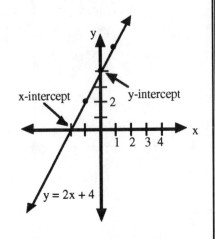

FT-50

ADDITION OF INTEGERS

If the signs are the same, combine by adding the absolute value of each number and keep the same sign.

If the signs are different, ignore them. Then subtract the smaller number from the larger number and keep the sign of the original number that has the larger absolute value.

Example 1:
   add -5 + (-3)
   |-5| = 5 and |-3| = 3
   5 + 3 = 8
   Both signs are –, so -5 + (-3) = -8

Example 2:
   add -4 + 2
   |-4| = 4 and |2| = 2
   4 – 2 = 2
   4 is greater than 2, so -4 + 2 = -2

Put your examples in the space below.

FT-88

RULE FOR SUBTRACTING INTEGERS

Adding the opposite of the second number gives the same answer as subtracting it.

Step One: Change the subtraction sign to an addition sign.

Step Two: Change the sign of the integer you are subtracting.

Step Three: Use the integer rules for addition.

Here is an example: $4 - (-5) = 4 + (+5) = 9$.

_____

_____

_____

_____

_____

FT-108

RULES FOR MULTIPLYING INTEGERS

If you multiply two integers with the **same sign**, the answer is **positive**.

If you multiply two integers with **different signs**, the answer is **negative**.

Examples: $(3)(5) = 15$; $(-3)(5) = -15$; $(-3)(-5) = 15$

_____

_____

_____

_____

FT-120

RULES FOR DIVIDING INTEGERS

The rules for determining the sign of the answer for division of integers are the **same as multiplication.**

If you divide two integers with the **same sign**, the answer is **positive**.

If you divide two integers with **different signs**, the answer is **negative.**

Examples: $6 \div 2 = 3$; $\frac{-8}{4} = -2$

_____

_____

_____

_____

_____

PROBABILITY

When you know all possible outcomes of an event, and all have the same chance of occurring, the **PROBABILITY** of an event is:

$$P(\text{event}) = \frac{\text{number of outcomes in the event}}{\text{number of possible outcomes}}$$

P(event) is the way we write that we want the probability "P" of a certain event. For example, there are 6 faces on a die. Suppose the desired event is to roll a 4. Since the number 4 appears once, we write the probability of getting a 4 as $P(4) = \frac{1}{6}$.

THEORETICAL PROBABILITY is calculated probability. If every outcome is equally likely, it is the ratio of outcomes in an event to all possible outcomes. For example, the probability of flipping a coin and getting "heads" is $\frac{1}{2}$ for each flip of a coin.

EXPERIMENTAL PROBABILITY is the probability based on data collected in experiments. For example, if you flip a coin 100 times, you will not always get 50 "heads" and 50 "tails" (the theoretical probability for 100 flips). If "heads" comes up 47 times, then the experimental probability of getting "heads" for the 100 flips would be $\frac{47}{100}$, which is close to the theoretical probability but not equal to it.

COMPOUND PROBABILITY deals with a combination of simple events.

• When either of two outcomes are specified (look for the word "or"), that is, either may happen but not both, find the probability of each specified outcome and add their probabilities.

• When both of two outcomes are specified (look for the word "and"), that is, the result must have both outcomes, find the probability of each outcome and multiply the probabilities.

Write P(odd number) in the space below, then create an example for both types of compound probability.

IDENTITY PROPERTY OF MULTIPLICATION
FINDING EQUIVALENT FRACTIONS

Any number multiplied by one (1) equals itself. This is the **IDENTITY PROPERTY OF MULTIPLICATION**. That is, for any number n,

$$n \cdot 1 = n$$

This property is used to make **EQUIVALENT FRACTIONS**, that is, fractions that are equal but are written in <u>different</u> <u>forms</u>.

In general, $\frac{a}{b} \cdot \frac{c}{c} = \frac{ac}{bc}$. For example: $\frac{2}{3} \cdot \frac{4}{4} = \frac{(2)(4)}{(3)(4)} = \frac{8}{12}$.

Put your example in the space below.

MULTIPLICATION OF FRACTIONS

To multiply fractions, multiply the numerators to make the new numerator and multiply the denominators to make the new denominator.

Use the Identity Property (find any Giant **1**s in the product) to simplify the resulting fraction.

In general, $\frac{a}{b} \cdot \frac{c}{d} = \frac{ac}{bd}$.

Examples:　$\frac{2}{3} \cdot \frac{1}{5} = \frac{2}{15}$

$\frac{3}{4} \cdot \frac{2}{3} = \frac{6}{12} = \frac{6}{6} \cdot \frac{1}{2} = \frac{1}{2}$

ADDING AND SUBTRACTING FRACTIONS

To add or subtract two fractions, the fractions must have the same denominator. One way to convert two fractions with different denominators into fractions with the same denominator is to use a Giant **1**. Below are examples of adding and subtracting two fractions with unlike denominators. In general,

$$\frac{a}{b} + \frac{c}{d} = \frac{a}{b} \cdot \boxed{\frac{d}{d}} + \frac{c}{d} \cdot \boxed{\frac{b}{b}} = \frac{ad}{bd} + \frac{bc}{bd} = \frac{ad+bc}{bd}$$

ADDITION

$$\frac{1}{5} + \frac{1}{3} = \frac{1}{5} \cdot \boxed{\frac{3}{3}} + \frac{1}{3} \cdot \boxed{\frac{5}{5}} = \frac{3}{15} + \frac{5}{15} = \frac{8}{15}$$

SUBTRACTION

$$\frac{3}{4} - \frac{1}{5} = \frac{3}{4} \cdot \boxed{\frac{5}{5}} - \frac{1}{5} \cdot \boxed{\frac{4}{4}} = \frac{15}{20} - \frac{4}{20} = \frac{11}{20}$$

Answer parts (a) and (b) in the space below.

FRACTIONS—DECIMALS—PERCENTS

Fractions, decimals, and percents are different ways to represent the same number.

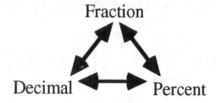

Fraction

Decimal   Percent

Examples:

Decimal to percent:

Multiply the decimal by 100.

$(0.34)(100) = 34\%$

Percent to decimal:

Divide the percent by 100.

$78.6\% \div 100 = 0.786$

Fraction to percent:

Set up an equivalent fraction using 100 as the denominator. The numerator is the percent.

$\frac{4}{5} = \frac{80}{100} = 80\%$

Percent to fraction:

Use 100 as the denominator. Use the percent as the numerator. Simplify as needed.

$22\% = 0.22 = \frac{22}{100} = \frac{11}{50}$

Decimal to fraction:

Use the decimal as the numerator. Use the decimal place value name as the denominator. Simplify as needed.

$0.2 = \frac{2}{10} = \frac{1}{5}$

Fraction to decimal:

Divide the numerator by the denominator.

$\frac{3}{8} = 3 \div 8 = 0.375$

ORDER OF OPERATIONS

An expression is organized into parts that are separated by addition (+) or subtraction (–) symbols <u>unless</u> the sum or difference is inside parentheses. Each part (a number, variable, product or quotient of numbers and variables) is called a **TERM**.

1. <u>Circle</u> the terms in the expression.

2. <u>Simplify</u> each term until it is one number by:

   • evaluating each exponential number.

   • performing each operation inside parentheses before doing any other operations in the term following the rule below.

   • multiplying and dividing from left to right.

3. Finally, <u>combine like terms</u> by adding and subtracting left to right.

Examples of a term include 4, 3x, $-2y^4$, $\frac{3x}{7}$, $4(x + 3)$, and $5x(x - 2)^2$.

Example:

Simplify $3(6 - 3) + 4 \cdot 5^2 - 10$.

$\widehat{3(6 - 3)} + \widehat{4 \cdot 5^2} - \widehat{10}$

$\widehat{3(3)} + \widehat{4 \cdot 5 \cdot 5} - \widehat{10}$

$\widehat{9} + \widehat{4 \cdot 25} - \widehat{10}$

$\widehat{9} + \widehat{100} - \widehat{10}$

$109 - 10 = 99$

Answer parts (a) and (b) in the space below.

DISTRIBUTIVE PROPERTY WITH INTEGERS

- Rewrite the multiplication problem as two or more terms of products to be added or subtracted.
- Multiply the separate parts.
- Add or subtract the products.

Example 1: $6 \cdot 37 = 6(30 + 7) = 6 \cdot 30 + 6 \cdot 7$
$= 180 + 42 = 222$

Example 2: $3 \cdot 715$

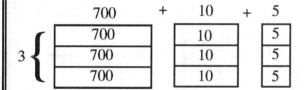

$3 \cdot 715$
$= 3(700 + 10 + 5)$
$= 3(700) + 3(10) + 3(5)$
$= 2100 + 30 + 15$
$= 2145$

$3 \cdot 715 = 2145$

HOW TO COMBINE LIKE TERMS

Group all of the tiles with the same area. Doing so models an algebraic process called **COMBINING LIKE TERMS**.

Note: The formal definition of **like terms** is two or more terms that have the same variable(s) with corresponding variable(s) raised to the same power.

Examples: 6 and 13, $2x^2$ and $-7x^2$, 4ab and 3ab.

<u>Not</u> like terms: 5 and 3x, 5x and $3x^2$, ab and ab^2.

List terms in order of decreasing powers.

Tile model:

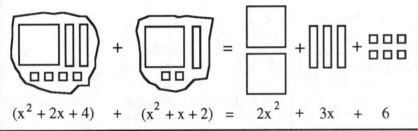

$$(x^2 + 2x + 4) \;+\; (x^2 + x + 2) \;=\; 2x^2 \;+\; 3x \;+\; 6$$

DISTRIBUTIVE PROPERTY WITH ALGEBRA TILES

Using the Distributive Property, the area of a rectangular arrangement of algebra tiles can be represented in three different ways.

$3x + 9$ $3(x) + 3(3)$ $3(x + 3)$

$$\text{area} \;=\; 3x + 9 \;=\; 3(x) + 3(3) \;=\; 3(x + 3)$$

In general, ab + ac = a(b) + a(c) = a(b + c)

WRITING EQUATIONS FROM A GUESS AND CHECK TABLE

- Make a Guess and Check table and solve the problem. Use at least four guesses, show all of your work, and write your answer in a complete sentence.

- Put an x in your Guess column and use x to write expressions in each of the other columns.

- Write your equation outside the Guess and Check table. You may need to use the Distributive Property and/or combine like terms.

Example: Noel and his sister, Brigitte, are both at camp. Noel is 3 years older than Brigitte, and the sum of their ages is 21. How old is Noel and how old is Brigitte? Use a Guess and Check table to solve for their ages. Write an equation.

Guess Brigitte's Age	Noel's Age	Sum of Noel and Brigitte's Ages	Check 21
10	(10) + 3 = 13	(10) + (13) = 23	too high
5	(5) + 3 = 8	(5) + (8) = 13	too low
8	(8) + 3 = 11	(8) + (11) = 19	too low
9	(9) + 3 = 12	(9) + (12) = 21	correct
x	x + 3	(x) + (x + 3) = 21	

$$(x) + (x + 3) = 2x + 3 = 21$$

Noel is 12 years old and Brigitte is nine years old.

Complete your Tool Kit response in the space below.

DISTRIBUTIVE PROPERTY

The **DISTRIBUTIVE PROPERTY** shows how to express sums and products in two ways: $a(b + c) = ab + ac$. This can also be written $(b + c) a = ab + ac$.

Factored form	Distributed form	Simplified form
a(b + c)	**a(b) + a(c)**	**ab + ac**

To simplify: Multiply each term on the inside of the parentheses by the term on the outside. Combine terms if possible.

To factor: Find a common factor that divides each term evenly. Then write this factor outside the parentheses and leave the remaining factors of each term written as a sum.

Note: An **integer factor** is an integer that divides another integer evenly.

Examples: Simplify: $5(x + 12)$ Factor: $4x + 6$ Factor: $6x + 3$

$$5(x + 12)$$
$$⑤(x) + ⑤(12)$$
$$5x + 60$$

$$4x + 6$$
$$2(2x) + 2(3)$$
$$②(2x) + ②(3)$$
$$2(2x + 3)$$

$$6x + 3$$
$$3(2x) + 3(1)$$
$$③(2x) + ③(1)$$
$$3(2x + 1)$$

Answer parts (a) through (c) in the space below.

_____

_____

_____

_____

DISTRIBUTING A NEGATIVE ONE

When a negative one (-1) is distributed to the terms inside a pair of parentheses, the sign of <u>each</u> term is changed. For example,

$$-(3x^2 + 2x - 5) \Rightarrow (-1)(3x^2 + 2x - 5)$$
$$\Rightarrow (-1)(3x^2) + (-1)(2x) - (-1)(5)$$
$$\Rightarrow -3x^2 - 2x + 5$$

_____

_____

_____

_____

MC-8

EQUATIONS

A mathematical sentence with an equal sign is called an **EQUATION**. It is a relationship showing that two expressions have the same value.

Statements like 16 ounces = 1 pound, $n = 4$, $3(x - 5) = 16$, and $3(2) + 7 = 16 - 3$ are examples of equations.

_____

_____

_____

MC-119

MIXED NUMBERS

The number $4\frac{1}{4}$ is called a **MIXED NUMBER** because it is made from a whole number, 4, and a fraction, $\frac{1}{4}$. It is a mix of a whole number and a fraction:

$$4\frac{1}{4} = \frac{16}{4} + \frac{1}{4} = \frac{17}{4}$$

The number $\frac{17}{4}$ is a fraction that is greater than 1 because the numerator is greater than the denominator. Sometimes fractions that are greater than one are called "improper fractions." "Improper" does not mean wrong. For mathematics, keeping a fraction in its "improper form" is often more useful than changing it to a mixed number.

RS-1

CONGRUENT

Two shapes (triangles, for example) are **CONGRUENT** if they have exactly the same size and shape.

RATIO

A **RATIO** is the comparison of two quantities by division. A ratio can be written as a fraction, in words, or with colon notation. (We will use the fraction form in this class.)

$$\frac{26 \text{ miles}}{1 \text{ gallon}} \qquad 26 \text{ miles to } 1 \text{ gallon} \qquad 26 \text{ miles : } 1 \text{ gallon}$$

A ratio: • should never be written as a mixed number.

• must have units labeled when the units are different.

PROPORTION

An equation stating that two ratios are equal is called a **PROPORTION**.

Examples: $\frac{2}{4} = \frac{3}{6}$, $\frac{5}{7} = \frac{50}{70}$, $\frac{154}{49} = \frac{44}{14}$

Write your explanation in the space below.

_____

_____

_____

_____

SOLVING PROPORTIONS WITH CROSS MULTIPLICATION

In a proportion, **CROSS MULTIPLICATION** is finding the product of the numerator (top) of one ratio and the denominator (bottom) of the other ratio, multiplying the other numerator and denominator together, and setting the products equal.

For any proportion $\frac{a}{b} = \frac{c}{d}$, after cross multiplication the result is $\mathbf{a \cdot d = b \cdot c}$.

Example: Use cross multiplication to solve for x in each proportion.

Step 1   Group any numerator and denominator elements together with parentheses if any part is a sum.

$$\frac{x}{30} = \frac{40}{100} \qquad \frac{(x+1)}{2} = \frac{3}{5}$$

Step 2   Cross multiply (multiply the numerator of each ratio by the denominator of the other ratio) to write an equation without fractions.

$$\frac{x}{30} \diagdown \frac{40}{100} \qquad \frac{(x+1)}{2} \diagdown \frac{3}{5}$$

$$x \cdot 100 = 30 \cdot 40 \qquad 5(x+1) = 2 \cdot 3$$

Step 3   Solve for x.

$$100x = 1200 \qquad 5x + 5 = 6$$

$$x = 12 \qquad 5x = 1$$

$$x = \frac{1}{5}$$

Solve the proportions in the space below.

a)	b)	c)

PARALLELOGRAM VOCABULARY

Two lines in a plane (flat surface) are **PARALLEL** if they never meet. The distance between the parallel lines is always the same. The marks >> indicate that the two lines are parallel.

The **DISTANCE** between two parallel lines or segments is indicated by a line segment perpendicular to both parallel lines (or segments).

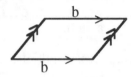

A **HEIGHT** (h) is the <u>perpendicular distance</u>:

- in triangles, from a vertex (corner) to the line containing the opposite side.

- in quadrilaterals, between two parallel sides or the lines containing those sides.

Any side of a two-dimensional figure may be used as a **BASE** (b).

A **PARALLELOGRAM** is a quadrilateral (a four-sided figure) with both pairs of opposite sides parallel.

PERCENTAGES

To solve a percentage problem you can use a proportion. There are four quantities to consider in your proportion: the percent (i.e., <u>part</u> of 100), 100, the whole, and a part of the whole. One of these quantities will be unknown.

Example: What number is 25% of 160?

$$\frac{\%}{100} = \frac{\text{part}}{\text{a whole}}$$

- Set up your proportion with the percent numbers on one side and the quantities you wish to compare on the other side.

$$\frac{25}{100} = \frac{x}{160}$$

- Cross multiply to write an equation without fractions.

$$25 \cdot 160 = 100x$$

- Solve for the unknown.

$$x = 40$$

AREA OF PARALLELOGRAMS, TRIANGLES, AND TRAPEZOIDS

Parallelogram

$$A = b \cdot h$$

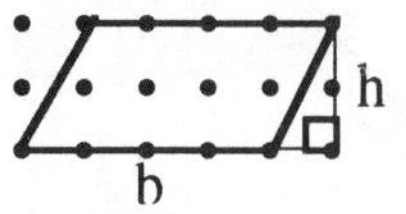

Triangle

$$A = \frac{1}{2} b \cdot h$$

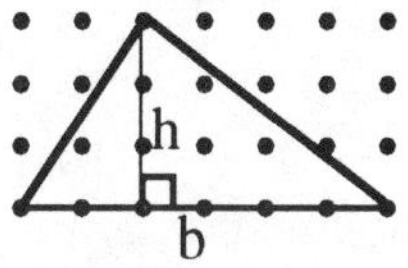

Trapezoid

$$A = \frac{1}{2} (b + t) \cdot h$$

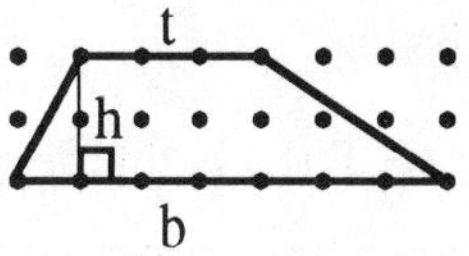

Calculate the area of each shape in the Tool Kit entry in the space below.

RS-62

CIRCUMFERENCE OF CIRCLES

The **CIRCUMFERENCE** (C) of a circle is its perimeter, that is, the "distance around" the circle.

To find the circumference of a circle from its **diameter** (d), use $C = \pi \cdot d$.

To find the circumference of a circle from its **radius** (r), use $C = 2\pi \cdot r$.

AREA OF CIRCLES

To find the **AREA** (A) of a circle when given its radius (r), use the formula

$$A = \pi \cdot r \cdot r = \pi r^2$$

_____

_____

_____

SIMILARITY AND SCALE FACTORS

Two figures are **SIMILAR** if they have the same shape but not necessarily the same size. In similar figures:

- the corresponding angles have the same measures *and*
- the ratios of all corresponding pairs of sides are equal.

The simplified ratio of any pair of corresponding sides in similar figures is called the **SCALE FACTOR**.

Example for two similar triangles:

$$\frac{AB}{DE} = \frac{16}{40} = \frac{2}{5}$$

$$\frac{BC}{EF} = \frac{10}{25} = \frac{2}{5}$$

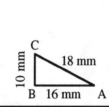

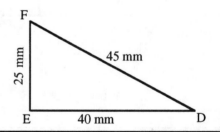

Answer parts (a) and (b) in the space below.

RATIOS OF SIMILARITY

When figures are similar, the ratio of the perimeters is the same as the scale factor, $\frac{a}{b}$.

The ratio of the areas is the square of the scale factor, $\left(\frac{a}{b}\right)^2$.

The **PERIMETER RATIO** is $\left(\frac{copy}{original}\right)$ = scale factor = $\frac{a}{b}$.

The **AREA RATIO** is $\left(\frac{copy}{original}\right)$ = (scale factor)^2 = $\left(\frac{a}{b}\right)^2$.

For example, in the figures at right, the scale factor is $\frac{3}{1}$.

The perimeter ratio is $\frac{30}{10} = \frac{3}{1}$ = scale factor.

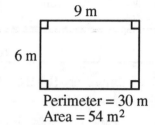

3 m

2 m

Perimeter = 10 m
Area = 6 m^2

9 m

6 m

Perimeter = 30 m
Area = 54 m^2

The area ratio is $\frac{54}{6} = \frac{9}{1} = \left(\frac{3}{1}\right)^2$ (the scale factor squared).

RECIPROCAL or MULTIPLICATIVE INVERSE

Two numbers with a product of 1 are called **RECIPROCALS** or **MULTIPLICATIVE INVERSES**.

Examples: The reciprocal of 3 is $\frac{1}{3}$; of $\frac{2}{5}$ is $\frac{5}{2}$; of $\frac{1}{7}$ is 7.

Answer the question in the space below.

SOLVING EQUATIONS WITH FRACTIONAL COEFFICIENTS

Once an equation has been simplified so that the variable is isolated with a fractional coefficient, divide both sides by the fractional coefficient or multiply both sides by its reciprocal.

Example 1: $\frac{1}{4}x = 12$

Solution A:

$$\frac{\frac{1}{4}x}{\frac{1}{4}} = \frac{12}{\frac{1}{4}}$$

$$x = 12 \div \frac{1}{4}$$

$$x = \frac{12}{1} \cdot \frac{4}{1}$$

$$x = 48$$

Solution B:

$$\frac{1}{4}x = 12$$

$$\frac{4}{1} \cdot \frac{1}{4}x = 12 \cdot \frac{4}{1}$$

$$x = \frac{48}{1}$$

$$x = 48$$

Example 2: $\frac{3}{4}x = 12$

Solution A:

$$\frac{\frac{3}{4}x}{\frac{3}{4}} = \frac{12}{\frac{3}{4}}$$

$$x = 12 \div \frac{3}{4}$$

$$x = \frac{12}{1} \cdot \frac{4}{3}$$

$$x = \frac{48}{3} = \frac{16}{1}$$

$$x = 16$$

Solution B:

$$\frac{3}{4}x = 12$$

$$\frac{4}{3} \cdot \frac{3}{4}x = 12 \cdot \frac{4}{3}$$

$$x = \frac{48}{3} = \frac{16}{1}$$

$$x = 16$$

DIVISION OF FRACTIONS

To divide fractions, multiply by the reciprocal of the divisor.

Example 1: $\dfrac{7}{6} \div \dfrac{2}{3} = \dfrac{7}{6} \cdot \dfrac{3}{2} = \dfrac{21}{12}$ or $\dfrac{7}{4}$

Example 2: $\dfrac{\frac{2}{3}}{\frac{5}{6}} = \dfrac{2}{3} \cdot \dfrac{6}{5} = \dfrac{12}{15}$ or $\dfrac{4}{5}$

SIMPLE INTEREST

SIMPLE INTEREST is interest paid only on the original amount of the principal at each specified interval (such as annually). The formula is $I = Prt$, where I = Interest, P = Principal, r = rate, and t = time.

Example: Teresa invested $1425.00 (principal) in a savings account at her local bank. The bank pays a simple interest of 3.5% annually (rate). How much money will Teresa have after 4 years (time)?

$$I = Prt \quad \Rightarrow \quad I = (1425)(0.035)(4) = \$199.50$$

$$\Rightarrow \quad P + I = \$1425 + \$199.50 = \$1624.50$$

Teresa will have $1624.50 after 4 years.

Answer part (a) in the space below.

COMPOUND INTEREST

COMPOUND INTEREST is interest paid on both the original principal and the interest earned previously.

The formula for compound interest is $A = P(1 + r)^t$, where A = total amount including previous interest earned, P = principal, r = interest rate, and t = time.

Example: Teresa found another bank that paid 3.5% (rate) compounded annually. If she invests $1425.00 (principal), how much money will she have after four years (time)?

$$A = P(1 + r)^t \implies A = 1425(1 + 0.035)^4$$
$$\implies 1425(1.035)^4 = 1425 \cdot 1.1475 = \$1635.22$$

Teresa will have $1635.22 after 4 years.

Answer the question in the space below.

_____

_____

_____

_____

MARKUP AND SELLING PRICES

The amount that the cost of an item will increase is called a **MARKUP**. This increase is based on a percentage of the cost.

The **SELLING PRICE** is the sum of the original cost and the markup.

Example:
The wholesale price of a pen is $0.70. To ensure a profit, Angela must mark up the wholesale price by 35%. Determine the markup and selling price.

$$\frac{\%}{100} = \frac{\text{part}}{\text{a whole}} \qquad \frac{35}{100} = \frac{m}{\$0.70} \qquad \text{markup} = \$0.2450 \approx \$0.25$$

$$\text{selling price} = \text{wholesale} + \text{markup} = \$0.70 + \$0.25 = \$0.95$$

DISCOUNT AND SALE PRICE METHODS

Method #1

- Determine the percent of discount.
- Write a proportion.
- Calculate the discount by solving the proportion.
- Subtract the discount from the original selling price.

  Your answer is the sale price.

Method #2

- Determine the percent of discount.
- Subtract the percent discount from 100%. This is the percentage to be paid.
- Write a proportion. Solve to find the sale price.

  Your answer is the sale price.

Example: Find the sale price of a $55 shirt sold at a 25% discount.

Method #1:

$$\frac{25}{100} = \frac{x}{55}$$
$$(100)(x) = (55)(25)$$
$$100x = 1375$$
$$x = \$13.75 \text{ (discount)}$$
$$\$55 - \$13.75 = \$41.25 = \text{sale price}$$

Method #2:

$$100\% - 25\% = 75\%$$
$$\frac{75}{100} = \frac{x}{55}$$
$$(100)(x) = (55)(75)$$
$$x = \$41.25$$

PERCENTAGE INCREASE OR DECREASE

Determine the amount of increase or decrease, then set up a proportion and solve for the percentage.

$$\frac{\text{amount of increase or decrease}}{\text{original price}} = \frac{\text{x (percent)}}{100}$$

Example 1:

Bread increased from $0.29 to $2.89.

$$\$2.89 - 0.29 = \$2.60$$

$$\frac{x}{100} = \frac{\$2.60}{\$0.29}$$

$$0.29x = 260$$

$$x \approx 897\%$$

Example 2:

Phones decreased from $59 to $4.95.

$$\$59 - \$4.95 = \$54.05$$

$$\frac{x}{100} = \frac{\$54.05}{\$59}$$

$$59x = 5405$$

$$x \approx 92\%$$

FORMULAS

A **formula** is a shorthand way of writing a general mathematical statement or rule. When writing formulas, variables are assigned to represent the various parts of the rule or statement.

a) _____

b) _____

c) _____

d) _____

e) _____

DISTANCE, RATE, TIME

DISTANCE (d) equals the product of the rate of speed (r) and the time (t).

$$d = r \cdot t$$

Example: Find the rate of speed of a passenger car if the distance traveled is 572 miles and the time elapsed is 11 hours.

$$572 \text{ miles} = r \cdot 11 \text{ hours} \implies \frac{572 \text{ miles}}{11 \text{ hours}} = \text{rate} \implies 52 \text{ miles/hour} = \text{rate}$$

Write your examples in the space below.

_____

_____

RIGHT TRIANGLES

A **RIGHT TRIANGLE** is a triangle in which the two shorter sides form a right angle. The shorter sides are called **LEGS**. Opposite the right angle is the third and longest side called the **HYPOTENUSE**.

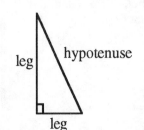

_____

_____

_____

MEASUREMENT IN DIFFERENT DIMENSIONS

Measurements in one dimension
are labeled as cm, ft, etc.

1 foot

Measurements in two dimensions
are labeled as cm^2, ft^2, etc.

1 foot

1 foot

1 ft x 1 ft = 1 ft^2

Measurements in three dimensions
are labeled as cm^3, ft^3, etc.

1 foot

1 foot

1 foot

1 ft x 1 ft x 1 ft = 1 ft^3

PYTHAGOREAN THEOREM

The **PYTHAGOREAN THEOREM** states that for any right triangle, the sum of the squares of the lengths of the legs is equal to the square of the length of the hypotenuse.

$(\textbf{leg 1})^2 + (\textbf{leg 2})^2 = (\textbf{hypotenuse})^2$

leg 1 ⟋ hypotenuse

leg 2

Example:

$(3)^2 + (4)^2 = (x)^2$
$9 + 16 = (x)^2$
$25 = (x)^2$
$5 = x$

Answer part (b) in the space below.

SQUARING AND SQUARE ROOT

When a number or variable is multiplied by itself, it is said to be **SQUARED**.

For example, $6 \cdot 6 = 6^2 = 36$, $a \cdot a = a^2$.

The **SQUARE ROOT** of a number or variable is the factor that when multiplied by itself results in the given number. Use a radical sign, $\sqrt{}$, to show this operation.

For example, $\sqrt{49}$ is read as "the square root of 49" and means, "Find the positive number that multiplied by itself equals 49." $\sqrt{49} = 7$, since $7 \cdot 7 = 49$.

When finding the area of a square you are squaring the number that represents the side length. When the area of a square is known, you determine its dimensions by finding the square root of a number.

Answer part (a) in the space below.

_____

_____

_____

BASES AND EXPONENTS

Bases and exponents are used to write a number or expression in **exponential form**: a^n. The **BASE**, a, is a factor (number or variable expression) raised to a power. The **EXPONENT**, n, is sometimes called the power and indicates how many times the base is used as a factor.

In general, a^n means a multiplied by itself n times. For example, 2^4 means $2 \cdot 2 \cdot 2 \cdot 2$. The base is 2 and the exponent is 4.

SUBPROBLEMS

Breaking a large or complex problem into smaller parts is a problem solving strategy called **SUBPROBLEMS**. This strategy means to solve each part and put the smaller parts back together to answer the original question.

Example: Find the area of this figure.

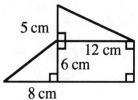

Subproblem 1:

$\frac{1}{2} \cdot 12 \cdot 5 = 30$
area of first triangle = 30 cm²

Subproblem 2:

$6 \cdot 12 = 72$
area of rectangle = 72 cm²

Subproblem 3:

$6 \cdot 8 = 48$
$48 \div 2 = 24$
area of second triangle = 24 cm²

Subproblem 4:

$30 + 72 + 24 = 126$
Sum of the areas = 126 cm²

Draw your figure and list the subproblems in the space below.

PRISMS

A **PRISM** is a three-dimensional figure composed of polygonal faces (called sides or lateral sides) and two congruent, parallel faces called bases. No holes are permitted in the solid. The remaining faces are parallelograms (or other special quadrilaterals). A prism is named for the shape of its base.

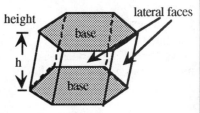

>>Problem continues on the next page.>>

You will need to fold these models flat for storage.

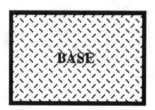

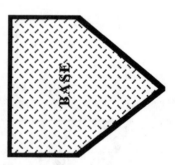

>>Problem continues on the next page.>>

TOOL KIT

VOLUME OF A PRISM

The **VOLUME** of a prism is the area of either base (A) times the height (h) of the prism.

$$V = \textbf{(Area of base)} \cdot \textbf{(height)}$$

$$V = Ah$$

Example:

Area of base $= (2 \text{ in.})(3 \text{ in.}) = 6 \text{ in.}^2$

(Area of base)(height) $= (6 \text{ in.}^2)(4 \text{ in.}) = 24 \text{ in.}^3$

Volume $= 24 \text{ in.}^3$

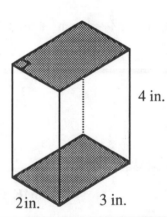

4 in.

2 in.   3 in.

Write your description in the space below.

SURFACE AREA OF A PRISM

The **SURFACE AREA** of a prism is the sum of the areas of all of the faces, including the bases. Surface area is expressed in **square units**.

Example: Find the surface area of the triangular prism at right.

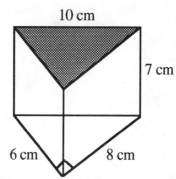

Subproblem 1: Area of the 2 bases

$$2\left[\frac{1}{2}(6 \text{ cm})(8 \text{ cm})\right] = 48 \text{ cm}^2$$

Subproblem 2: Area of the 3 sides
(lateral faces)

Area of side 1: (6 cm)(7 cm) = 42 cm^2
Area of side 2: (8 cm)(7 cm) = 56 cm^2
Area of side 3: (10 cm)(7 cm) = 70 cm^2

Subproblem 3: Surface Area of Prism = sum of bases and lateral faces

48 cm^2 + 42 cm^2 + 56 cm^2 + 70 cm^2 = 216 cm^2

VOLUME OF A CYLINDER

The **VOLUME OF A CYLINDER** is found by multiplying the base area (A) times the height (h).

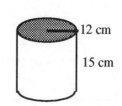

Volume = (Area of base)(height)
$$V = Ah = (\pi r^2)(h)$$

Example:

Find the volume of the cylinder at right.

$A = \pi(12)^2 = 144\pi$
$V = 144\pi(15) = 2160\pi \approx 6785.84 \text{ cm}^3$

SURFACE AREA OF A CYLINDER

The **SURFACE AREA OF A CYLINDER** is the sum of the two base areas and the l̶
surface area. The formula for the surface area is:

$$\text{S.A.} = 2\pi r^2 + \pi dh$$
$$= 2\pi r^2 + 2\pi rh$$

where r = radius, d = diameter, and h = height of the cylinder.

Example:

    Find the surface area of the cylinder at right.

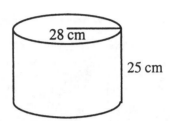

25 cm

    Subproblem 1:   Area of the two circular bases

    $2[\pi(28\text{ cm})^2] = 1568\pi \text{ cm}^2$

    Subproblem 2:   Area of the lateral face

    $\pi(56)25 = 1400\pi \text{ cm}^2$

    Subproblem 3:   Surface area of the cylinder

    $1568\pi \text{ cm}^2 + 1400\pi \text{ cm}^2 = 2968\pi \text{ cm}^2$
                                 $\approx 9324.25 \text{ cm}^2$

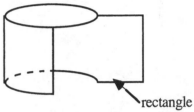

circumference of base

25 cm

Answer parts (a) and (b) in the space below.

RATE OF CHANGE

...hat compares the amount one quantity changes as another

$$\text{...hange} = \frac{\text{change in one quantity}}{\text{change in the other quantity}}$$

SLOPE OF A LINE AND LINEAR EQUATIONS

The **SLOPE** of a line is the rate of change between any two points on that line. It represents both steepness and direction. The slope ratio states the rate at which the relation between the two quantities is changing. The sign of the ratio indicates whether the rate of change is increasing (+) or decreasing (–).

$$\textbf{slope} = \frac{\text{vertical change}}{\text{horizontal change}} = \frac{\text{change in y-values}}{\text{change in x-values}}$$

Some textbooks write the ratio $\frac{\text{vertical change}}{\text{horizontal change}}$ as $\frac{\text{rise}}{\text{run}}$.

All equations of straight lines can be put in the form

$$y = (\textbf{coefficient})x + (\textbf{constant number})$$

where the **coefficient of x** is the rate of change (or **slope**), and the **constant number** is the **y-intercept**.

This form of a linear equation is called the **SLOPE-INTERCEPT FORM** and is written $y = mx + b$, where m is the slope and b is the y-coordinate of the y-intercept (0, b).

Example:

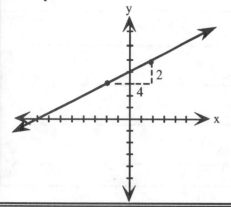

$$\text{slope} = \frac{\text{vertical change}}{\text{horizontal change}} = \frac{5 - 3}{2 - (-2)} = \frac{2}{4} = \frac{1}{2}$$

$$\text{y-intercept} = (0, 4)$$

$$y = \frac{1}{2}x + 4$$

RATIOS OF DIMENSIONAL CHANGE

For any pair of similar figures or solids with a scale factor $\frac{a}{b}$, the enlargement and reduction relationships are:

Length (one dimension)	Area (two dimensions)	Volume (three dimensions)
$\frac{a}{b}$	$\frac{a^2}{b^2}$	$\frac{a^3}{b^3}$

Example 1:

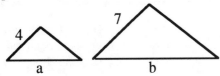

length: $\frac{a}{b} = \frac{4}{7}$

area: $\frac{a^2}{b^2} = \frac{4^2}{7^2} = \frac{16}{49}$

Example 2:

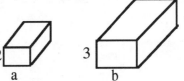

length: $\frac{a}{b} = \frac{2}{3}$

area: $\frac{a^2}{b^2} = \frac{2^2}{3^2} = \frac{4}{9}$

volume: $\frac{a^3}{b^3} = \frac{2^3}{3^3} = \frac{8}{27}$

Length ratios apply to sides, edges, and perimeters of figures.

Area ratios apply to surface area of solids and the area of two-dimensional regions.

VOLUME OF A CONE

Every cone has a volume that is one-third the volume of the cylinder with the same base and height. To find the volume of a cone, use the same formula as the volume of a cylinder and divide by three. The formula for the volume of a cone of base area A and height h is:

$$V = \frac{A \cdot h}{3}$$

When the base of the cone is a circle of radius r, the formula is:

$$V = \frac{\pi r^2 h}{3} \quad \text{or} \quad \frac{1}{3}\pi r^2 h$$

LAWS OF EXPONENTS

$$x^a \cdot x^b = x^{(a+b)} \qquad (x^a)^b = x^{ab} \qquad \frac{x^a}{x^b} = x^{(a-b)}$$

$$x^0 = 1 \qquad (x^a y^b)^c = x^{ac}y^{bc}$$

These rules hold if $x \neq 0$ and $y \neq 0$.

SCIENTIFIC NOTATION

SCIENTIFIC NOTATION is a way of writing very large and very small numbers compactly. A number is said to be in scientific notation when it is written as the product of two factors as described below.

- The first factor is less than 10 and greater than or equal to 1.
- The second factor has a base of 10 and an integer exponent (power of 10).
- The factors are separated by a multiplication sign.
- A positive exponent indicates a number whose absolute value is greater than one.
- A negative exponent indicates a number whose absolute value is less than one.

Scientific Notation	Standard Form
$5.32 \cdot 10^{11}$	532,000,000,000
$2.61 \cdot 10^{-15}$	0.00000000000000261

Write the numbers in the space below.

a) _____   b) _____